This book belongs to:

First paperback edition June 2021

Edited by Rebecca Michael
Book design by FolksnFables (Team: Neethi Joseph, Indu Shaji, Anuchand Ram)

ISBN 978-1-7373141-0-3 (paperback)

www.PingandBirdPublishing.com

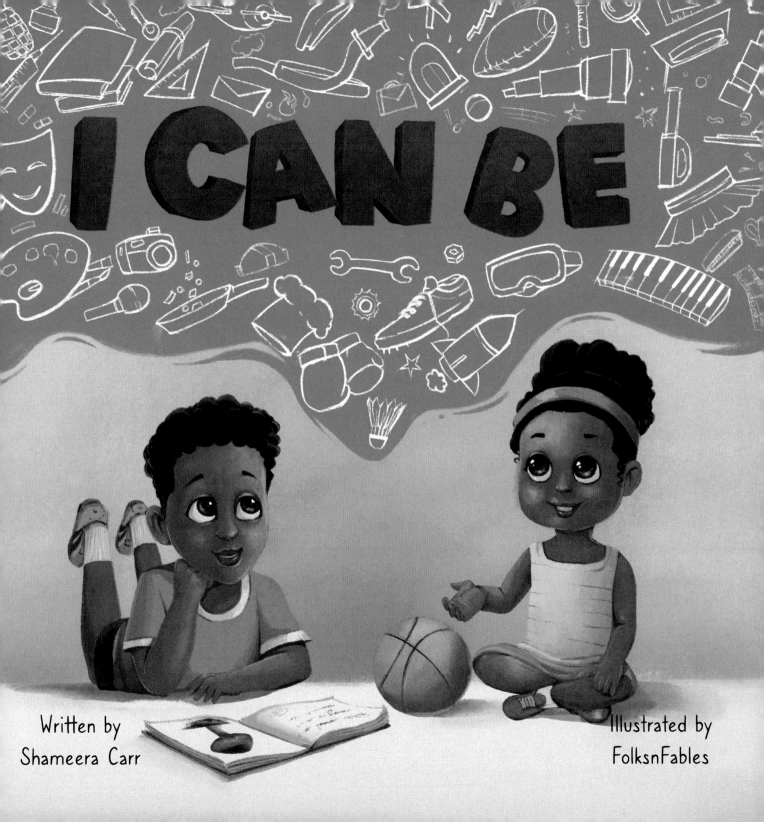

Dedication

To my parents
It is because of you that I can be.

When I look at the stars in the midnight sky,
I admire the moon perched way up high.
I can blast in a rocket beyond earth's hem,
I can be an astronaut like Mae Jemison.

I can be an artist, so poised and free,
Paint a president on canvas like Kehinde Wiley.

I can float like a butterfly and can sting like a bee,
Lacing gloves that I wear like Muhammad Ali.

I can dance like Misty Copeland, so bold on the stage,
All the eyes are on me, but I'm not afraid.
I perform my ballet in graceful motion,
Movements smooth, and they flow as the ocean.

I can pour sweet sounds from deep in my soul,

Singing, "It's a new dawn," just like Nina Simone.

I can conquer adversity with grace and determination,
And like Nelson Mandela, I can lead a whole nation.

Like young Ruby Bridges, I act brave and strong,
I am never afraid to walk alone.
I am guided by my inner light,
And my future holds promise that is so bright.

There is power in my words, and there's knowledge in my crown,
Like Jesse Owens, beating hurdles by leaps and bounds.

I can be a fine poet, as Amanda Gorman,
Standing proud and tall at the inaugural podium.

And like Chadwick Boseman, I'll bring characters to life,
Will inspire other actors to reach new heights.
I can be the king of Wakanda forever,
I can be a protector like the Black Panther.

I can fly like Bessie Coleman, as the pilot of my dreams,
There is nothing here to stop me, as long as I believe.

I will be as an eagle and soar through the sky,
There is no limit to what I can be if I try!

The End

What can you be?

I can be

_____

About the author

Shameera Carr was born and raised in Charlottesville, located in the beautiful Blue Ridge Mountain state of Virginia. Shameera considers her faith and family to be most important to her. When she is not with friends or family, you can almost always find her with a hot cup of tea and a good book.

I Can Be is Shameera's first children's book, which she wrote to give inclusion and representation to children of color. She aspires to empower, uplift, and encourage young readers to not only dream but also dream big. She hopes her books water the seeds of potential that exist within every child and spark unlimited growth.

Sign up for new book releases from this
Author at www.booksbymeera.com

@ShameeraCarr

Shameera L. Carr

Made in the USA
Monee, IL
17 February 2022